To Noah,

I'm so proud I
was your teacher.
I've watched you
learn and grow.
We worked so hard
and had such fun.
How fast the year did go!
We had so many special
times, but now it's
time to part.
Just know that you
will always have a
special place within
my heart!

Have a great time in Primary 2!

From Miss Rai ☺ 2021

First, **I** saw the white bear,
then **I** saw the black.

Then I saw the camel with a hump upon his back.

Then I saw the grey wolf,
food hanging from his jaws.

Then **I** saw the wombat,
waddling in the straw.

Then **I** saw the penguins,
sliding on the ice.

Then I saw the coyote, chasing after mice.

Then I saw the giraffes, their heads way up high.

Then I saw the koalas,
they're very, very shy.

Then I saw the leopards –
they never change their spots!

Then I saw the cheetahs, all covered up with dots.

Then **I** saw the llama,
his **coat** was nice and fluffy.

Then I saw the hyena –
he looked so very scruffy!

Then I saw the gazelle, jumping as she ran.

Then I saw the peacock,
his tail was like a fan.

Now it is time for us
to leave the zoo.

I really loved the animals,
I hope that you did, too!